Which Princess is different?

A

B

C

D

Your answer: ☐

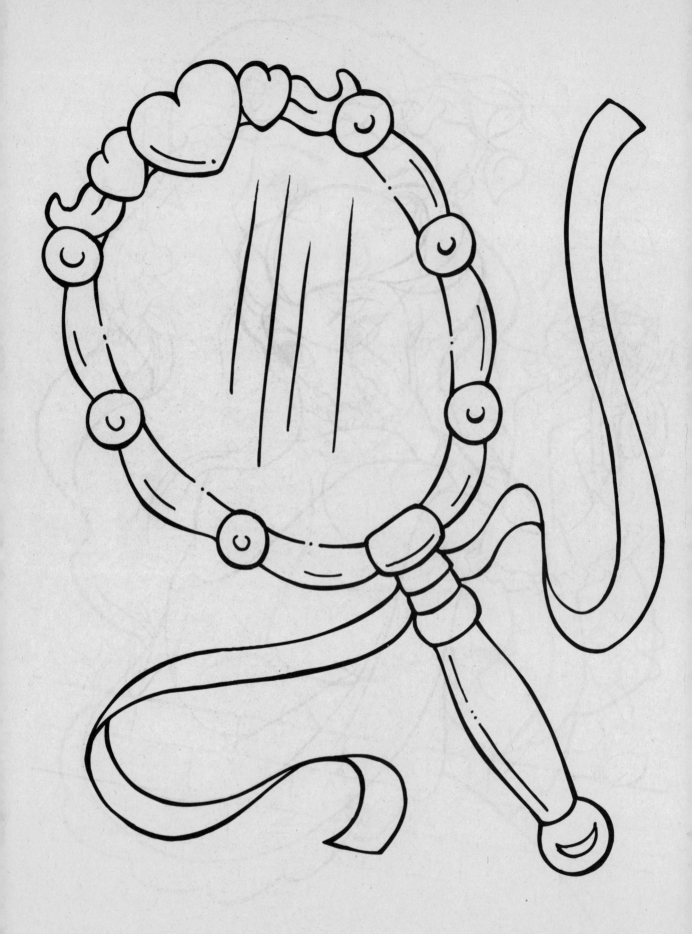

Finish the picture.

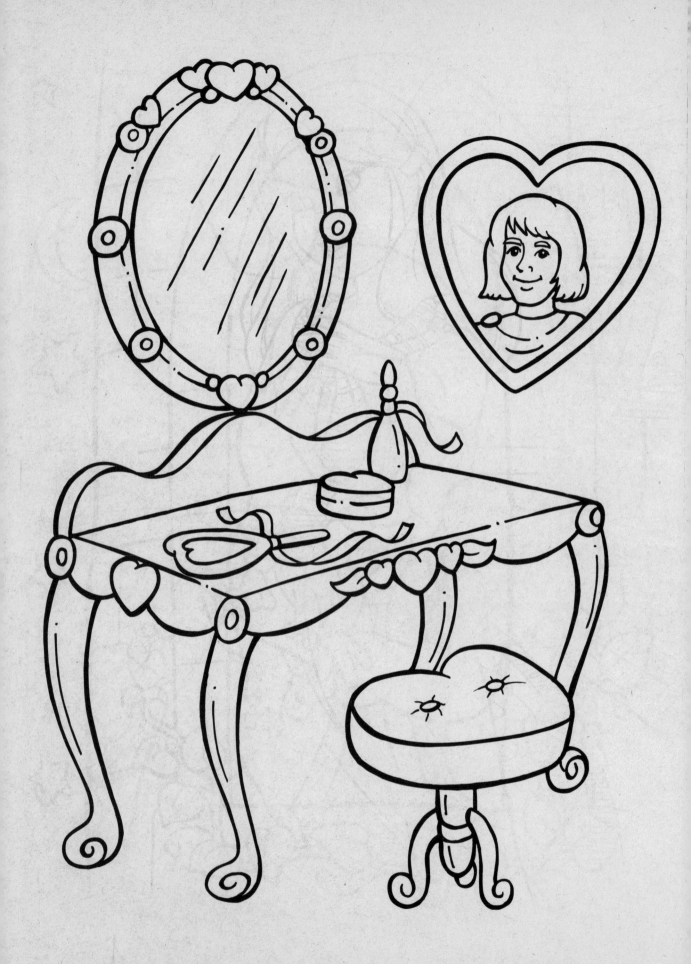

How many words can you make from the letters in:

WISE PRINCESS

Help Princess Isabel find her way home.

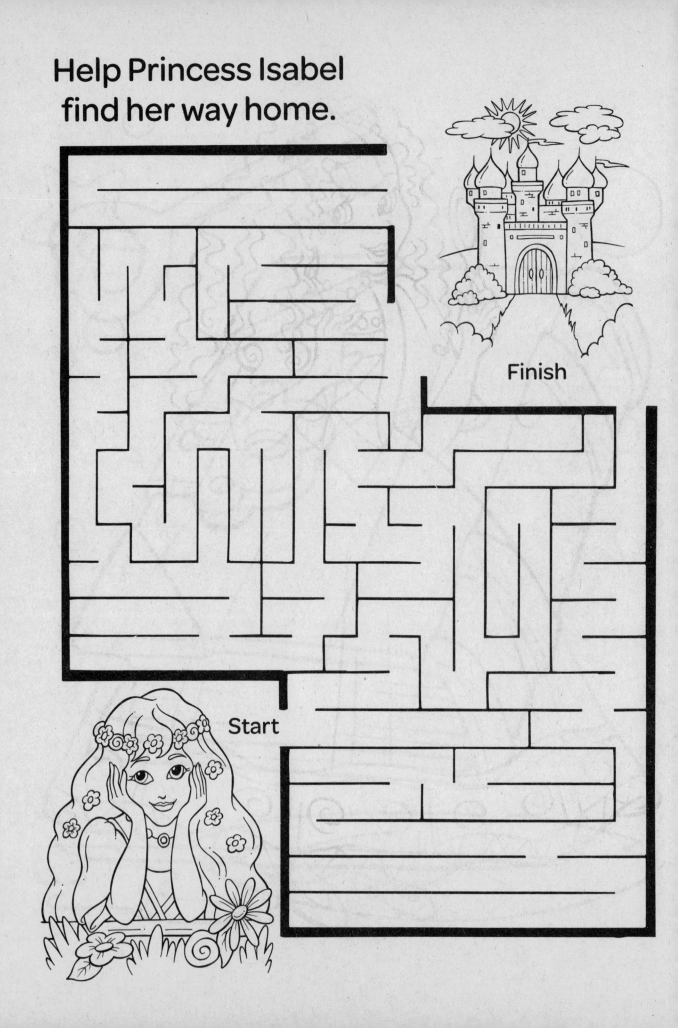

Finish

Start

Unscramble the princess words.

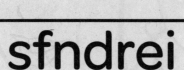

_____

sfndrei

_____

nicerp

_____

yalro

_____

miracghn

Royal Tic Tac Toe

Which pair of shoes is different?

A

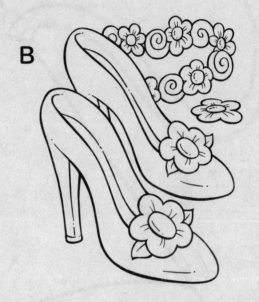

B

C

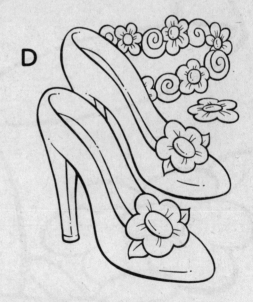

D

Your answer:

Draw yourself as a princess!

Use the grid to draw Princess Danielle.

Unscramble the princess words.

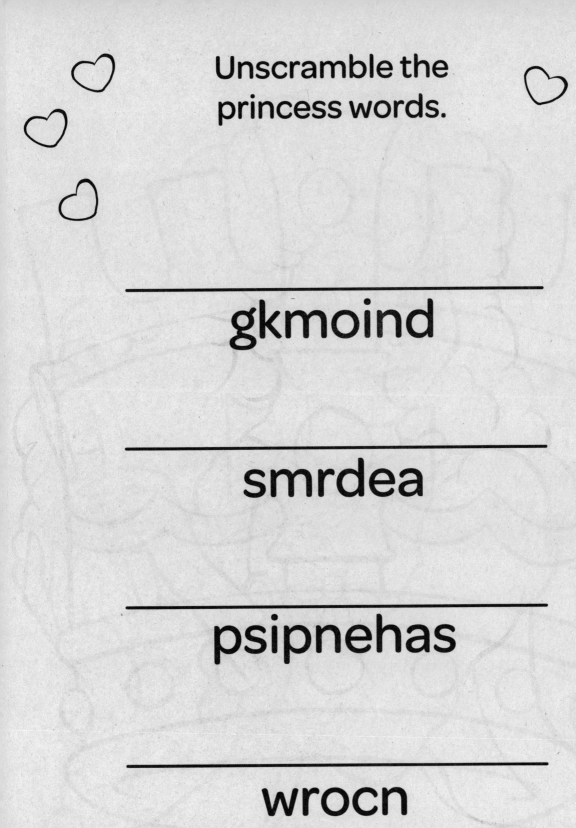

_____

gkmoind

_____

smrdea

_____

psipnehas

_____

wrocn

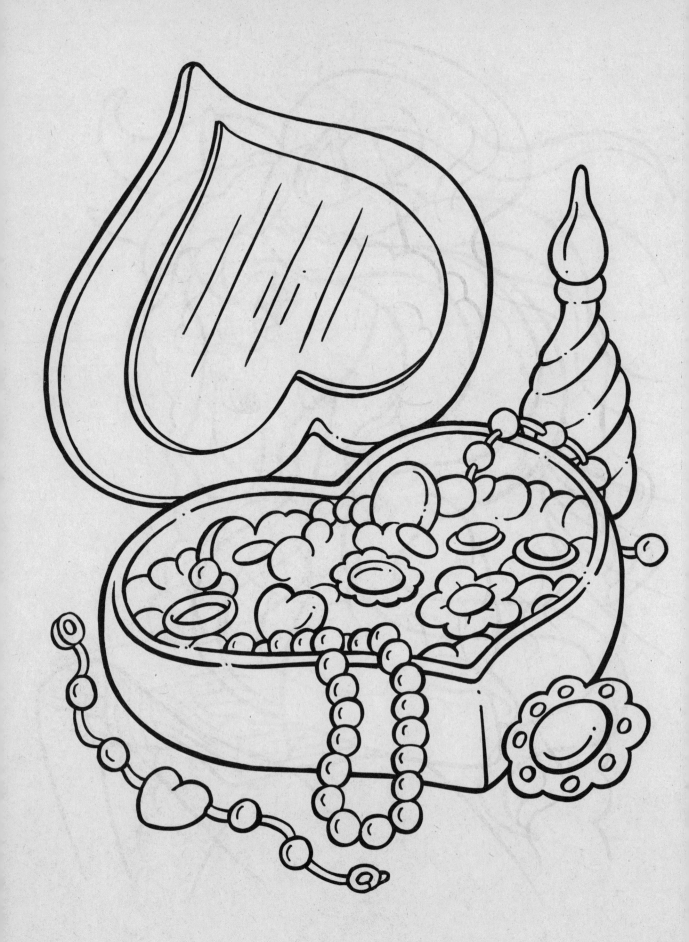

Use the grid to draw Princess Annabelle.

Royal Tic Tac Toe

Which royal ring is different?

Your answer: